THE MINIATURE SCORE SERIES

THE SYMPHONIES OF BRAHMS AND TSCHAIKOWSKY IN SCORE

Edited and devised by

ALBERT E. WIER

The system of arrow signals and special typographical markings, employed
in this work to enable those unacquainted with the art of score reading to
follow the instrumental outline and to identify the various themes as they
appear and recur, is the subject of a pending application for Letters Patent
of the United States owned by Harcourt, Brace and Company, Inc.

BONANZA BOOKS • NEW YORK

PREFACE

For the comprehension of orchestral scores, even with the assistance of the system of arrow signals employed in this volume, ability to read instrumental music in both treble and bass clefs is necessary.

It must also be borne in mind that certain wind instruments, such as the clarinet (except the clarinet in (C), the French horn (except the horn in C) and the trumpets (except the trumpet in C) are transposing instruments; also that viola and Tenor trombone parts are written in the Alto and Tenor clefs, therefore some knowledge of transposition and of these clefs will be useful.

Four separate pages of miniature score are printed on each large page of this volume. The large page is bisected by horizontal and vertical lines, the miniature pages located numerically as follows:

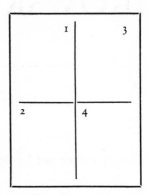

The large pages of this volume are designated by numbers in parentheses at the bottom of the pages; the miniature score pages of each symphony are numbered separately (starting with Page 1) in the upper right and left hand corners.

Turning to Page 6, containing the first four pages in miniature of the score for the First Symphony, it will be noted that Page 1 (on the miniature page) contains five bars of music with a separate line provided for each instrument, the name being noted before the line. On Page 3 of the miniature score it will be noted that two sections of scoring are given—each comprising six measures. This is known as score condensation, that is, all instruments that have no notes to play during the six measures of the first section on the page are omitted, and all instruments that have no notes to play in the six measures of the second section are omitted. The presence of two or more sections of scoring on one page is always indicated by the mark // between each section, and these marks must be carefully observed when reading score.

The system of arrow signals used in this volume will be easily comprehended if its purpose is fully understood before attempting to make use of them. The purpose, starting with the first measure of each symphony, is to indicate the main melodic line as it progresses from instrument to instrument in the wood-wind, brass, string and percussion sections of the orchestra. A practical example of this method of score-reading is given on the opposite page (Page 3).

In addition to the arrow signal system, the various divisions of each symphonic movement, such as **Introduction, Exposition, Development, Recapitulation, Coda, etc.** are indicated *over* the score; the names and lengths of the various themes, such as **Principal Theme, Subordinate Theme, Concluding Theme, etc.** are printed *under* the score with a wavy black line to indicate their length.

EXPLANATION OF ARROW SIGNAL SYSTEM

The pages used here for explanatory purposes are taken from the Andante of the First Symphony by Johannes Brahms.

The circled numbers near the arrows are used *only on this page* to aid in clarifying the explanation; they are not used elsewhere in the volume.

Arrows Nos. 1 & 2 indicate the appearance of the Principal Theme, Part I in the 1st violins and bassoon. At the bottom of the page is the name of the theme, the wavy black line indicating its length.

Arrow No. 3 indicates the continuance of the theme in the 1st violins.

Arrow No. 4 points out a figuration in the 'cellos and basses.

Arrow No. 5 indicates the continuance of the theme in the 1st violins.

Arrow No. 6 guides the eye in finding its place on the 1st violin line for the continuance of the theme on the next page of the score.

The Mark // indicates the separation of the page into two sections of score.

Arrow No. 7 guides the eye in finding its place on the 1st violin line in the second score section.

Arrow No. 8 indicates the removal of the melodic line to the flutes.

Arrow No. 9 indicates the return of the melodic line to the 1st violins.

Arrow No. 10 indicates the removal of the melodic line to the oboes.

SPECIAL NOTE

When two or more arrows are marked in the same measure, it means that the passage is to be found in other instruments at the same time, or that an important counter-theme or special musical figure is being developed. The eye can follow any one of these arrows.

INDEX

SYMPHONY No. 1, in C Minor, Op. 68   *JOHANNES BRAHMS*

MOVEMENTS:

1. *Un poco sostenuto—Allegro*
2. *Andante sostenuto*
3. *Un poco allegretto e grazioso*
4. *Adagio—Piu Andante—Allegro non troppo, ma con brio*

The metronome marks for this symphony are indicated by the composer.

Symphony No. 1 is scored for the following instruments:

2 Flöten (Flutes)	*Fl.*	2 Trompeten (Trumpets)	*Tr.*
2 Hoboen (Oboes)	*Hb.*	2 Pauken (Tympani)	*Pk.*
2 Klarinetten (Clarinets)	*Kl.*	1. Violinen (1st Violins)	*Vl.*
2 Fagotte (Bassoons)	*Fg.*	2. Violinen (2nd Violins)	
1 Kontrafagott (Double Bassoon)	*Kfg.*	Bratschen (Violas)	*Br.*
		Violoncelli (Violoncellos)	*Vc.*
4 Hörner (Horns)	*Hr.*	Kontrabässe (Double Basses)	*Kb.*

Each instrument is listed above under its name in German (as printed on the first page of the score); its English equivalent, and the abbreviation used on succeeding pages of the score.

Johannes Brahms was forty-three years of age when he completed the Symphony in C Minor, Op. 68, but he had been working on it for nearly twenty years. Sketches for an earlier symphony on which he was working as early as 1854 finally were transformed into the first movement of the piano concerto, Op. 15.

The first performance of the Symphony in C Minor, Op. 68 took place at Carlsruhe on November 4, 1876, the orchestra being under the direction of Otto Dessoff.

Critical opinion of both personal friends and music journalists varied in their estimates of the work. Clara Schumann wrote in her diary: "I cannot disguise the fact that I am painfully disappointed; in spite of its workmanship I feel it lacks melody". The critic Hanslick in the *Neue Freie Presse* said: "Brahms' artistic kinship with Beethoven must be plain to every observer". On the other hand the critic of the *Weinerzeitung* admitted the great personality shown in the work, but also speaks of the absence of imagination and of emotional attractiveness. Several critics drew attention to the similarity of the Principal Theme in the last movement to the theme used by Beethoven in the Finale in the Ninth Symphony.

Symphonie No 1

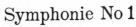

BRIDGE PASSAGE

PRINCIPAL THEME—PART I

EXPOSITION
Allegro

BASIC PHRASE

50

PRINCIPAL THEME

— PART II, 1st PERIOD ~~~~~~~~~~~~~~~~~~~~~~~~~

~~~~~~~~ PRINCIPAL THEME—PART III, 1st PERIOD ~~~~~~~~

~~~~~~~~ PRINCIPAL THEME—PART II, 2nd PERIOD ~~~~~~~~

~~~~~~~~ PRINCIPAL THEME—PART III, 2nd PERI

CONCLUDING THEME (CODETTA)—PART I

CONCLUDING THEME

DEVELOPMENT

(CODETTA)—PART II

DEVELOPMENT—SECTION I

DEVELOPMENT—SECTION 2 〰〰

DEVELOPMENT—SECTION 3 〰〰

RETURN BASIC PHRASE   RETURN PRINCIPAL

RETURN PRINCIPAL THEME—PART II, 1st PERIOD

42

THEME—PART I

44

RETURN PRINCIPAL

370 zu 2

THEME—PART II, 2nd PERIOD 〰〰〰〰

〰〰〰RETURN BRIDGE PASSAGE—SECTION I 〰〰〰

380

RETURN BRIDGE

390

PASSAGE—SECTION 2 〰〰〰〰

RETURN SUBORDINATE THEME—PART I 〰〰〰

400

RETURN SUBORDINATE THEME—PART II 〰〰〰

410

〰〰〰〰〰〰〰〰〰

(17)

CONCLUDING THEME (CODETTA)—PART II   CODA—SECTION I 〰〰〰〰

CODA—SECTION 2 〰〰〰〰

BRIDGE PASSAGE

SUBORDINATE THEME

PRINCIPAL THEME—PART II

(21)

BRIDGE PASSAGE

RETURN PRINCIPAL THEME—PART I

(22)

CODA—SECTION 2

SECOND SUBORDINATE THEME—PART II, 1st PERIOD

SECOND SUBORDINATE THEME—PART II, 2nd PERIOD

RETURN PRINCIPAL THEME—PART II 〰〰〰〰〰〰

RETURNING PASSAGE (RETRANSITION) 〰〰〰〰

RETURN PRINCIPAL THEME—PART I 〰〰〰〰〰〰〰〰〰〰

INTRODUCTION IV
Adagio

INTRODUCTION—SECTION I 〰〰〰

CODA
più tranquillo

string. poco a poco

in tempo

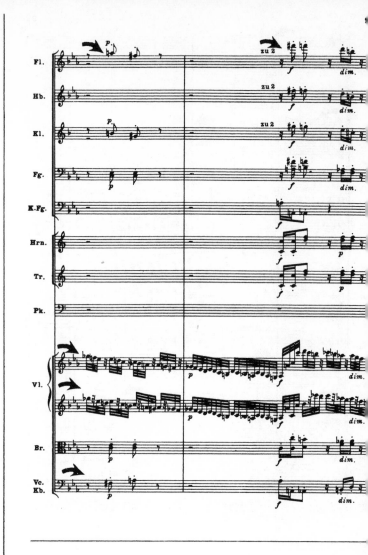

INTRODUCTION—SECTION 2 〰〰〰

30 Più Andante

f sempre e passionato

INTRODUCTION—SECTION 3 ∿∿∿∿

f sempre e passionato

INTRODUCTION—SECTION 4 ∿∿∿∿

50

INTRODUCTION—SECTION 5 ∿∿∿

SUBORDINATE THEME—PART I

SUBORDINATE THEME—PART II

(34)

CONCLUDING THEME (CODETTA)—PART I

(35)

CONCLUDING THEME (CODETTA)—PART II

RETURNI

RECAPITULATION

PASSAGE (RETRANSITION) RETURN PRINCIPAL THEME—PART I

RETURN PRINCIPAL THEME—

PART III

RETURN PRINCIPAL THEME—PART II

(39)

145

147

146

148

(42)

RETURN CONCLUDING THEME (CODETTA)—PART II 〰〰〰〰〰〰〰〰

(43)

(44)

Più Allegro

CODA—SECTION 3

CODA—SECTION 4

CODA—SECTION 5 〰〰〰

CODA—SECTION 6

MOVEMENTS:

1. *Allegro non troppo*
2. *Adagio non troppo*
3. *Allegretto grazioso (quasi andantino)*
4. *Allegro con spirito*

The metronome marks for this symphony are indicated by the composer.

Symphony No. 2 is scored for the following instruments:

2 Flöten (Flutes)	*Fl.*		1 Basstuba (Bass Tuba)	*Bsstb.*
2 Hoboen (Oboes)	*Hb.*		2 Pauken (Tympani)	*Pk.*
2 Klarinetten (Clarinets)	*Kl.*		1. Violinen (1st Violins)	*Vl.*
2 Fagotte (Bassoons)	*Fg.*		2. Violinen (2nd Violins)	
4 Hörner (Horns)	*Hr.*		Bratschen (Violas)	*Br.*
2 Trompeten (Trumpets)	*Tr.*		Violoncelli (Violoncellos)	*Vc.*
3 Posaunen (Trombones)	*Pos.*		Kontrabässe (Double Basses)	*Kb.*

Each instrument is listed above under its name in German (as printed on the first page of the score); its English equivalent, and the abbreviation used on succeeding pages of the score.

Johannes Brahms began work on his second symphony in D Major, Op. 73 during the summer of 1877. As the first symphony was extremely deep in character, he derived a great deal of satisfaction in misleading his friends and even his publisher, Fritz Simrock, as to the nature of the new work, writing him: "The new symphony is so melancholy that you will not be able to bear it". The facts are that the second symphony is in direct contrast to the almost tragic mood of the first; it is cheerful and bright in character.

The first performance of the Symphony in D Major, Op. 73, took place at Vienna on December 30, 1877. It was played by the Vienna Philharmonic Orchestra under the direction of Hans Richter. Critical opinion of both personal friends and the music press in Austria and Germany was almost unanimously favorable.

Symphonie № 2

I

EXPOSITION
Allegro non troppo

Johannes Brahms, Op 73
1833-1897

PRINCIPAL THEME—PART I, 1st PERIOD 〰〰〰

PRINCIPAL THEME—PART II ⌇⌇

PRINCIPAL THEME—PART I, 2nd PERIOD 〰〰〰〰

(49)

BRIDGE PASSAGE

SUBORDINATE THEME—PART I

SUBORDINATE THEME—PART II

CONCLUDING THEME (CODETTA)—PART I 〰〰

THEME (CODETTA)—PART II 〰〰〰〰〰〰〰〰〰

CONCLUDING

(51)

THEME (CODETTA)—PART III

DEVELOPMENT—SECTION 3

DEVELOPMENT—SECTION 4

RETURNING PASSAGE (RETRANSITION) 〰〰〰

RECAPITULATION

RETURN PRINCIPAL THEME—PART I 〰〰〰

30

32

SUBORDINATE THEME 〰〰〰〰〰〰〰〰〰〰〰〰〰〰

RETURN CONCLUDING THEME (CODETTA)

RETURN CONCLUDING THEME (CODETTA)—PART I

RETURN CONCLUDING THEME (CODETTA)—PART III〰

CODA

CODA—SECTION I

PRINCIPAL THEME—PART II

L'istesso tempo, ma grazioso

SUBORDINATE THEME—PART I

BRIDGE PASSAGE

SUBORDINATE THEME—PART II

SUBORDINATE THEME—PART III

CONCLUDING PASSAGE

(CODETTA)

muta G in Fis

RETRANSITION WITH DEVELOPMENT

zu 2

PRINCIPAL THEME—PART II

CODA

CODA—SECTION 1 〰〰〰

CODA—SECTION 2 〰〰〰

III
PRINCIPAL DIVISION

Presto ma non assai

REPETITION PRINCIPAL

PRINCIPAL DIVISION REPEATED

RETURN PRINCIPAL THEME—PART I

RETURN PRINCIPAL

THEME—PART III

THEME—PART II

RETURN PRINCIPAL THEME—PART III

THEME—PART I, 1st PERIOD

(72)

CONCLUDING THEME (CODETTA)—PART I

CONCLUDING THEME

(CODETTA)—PART II ᜠᜠᜠᜠᜠᜠᜠᜠᜠ

106

DEVELOPMENT—SECTION I ᜠᜠᜠ pp sempre

107

DEVELOPMENT—SECTION 2 ᜠᜠ

108

DEVELOPMENT—SECTION 3 ᜠᜠ

Tranquillo

DEVELOPMENT—SECTION 4 ∿∿∿∿

BRIDGE PASSAGE 〜〜〜 RETURN SUBORDINATE

THEME—PART I 〜〜〜〜〜〜〜〜〜〜〜〜〜〜〜〜〜

RETURN SUBORDINATE THEME—PART II ∿∿∿∿∿∿∿∿∿∿∿

RETURN CONCLUDING THEME (CODETTA)–

—PART I ∿∿∿∿∿∿∿∿∿∿∿∿∿∿∿

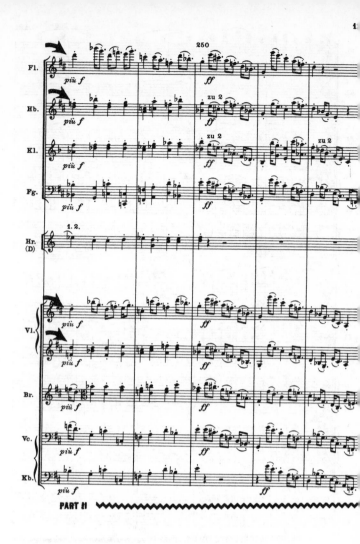

RETURN CONCLUDING THEME (CODETTA)-

CODA—SECTION 2

CODA—SECTION 3

CODA—SECTION 4 〰〰〰

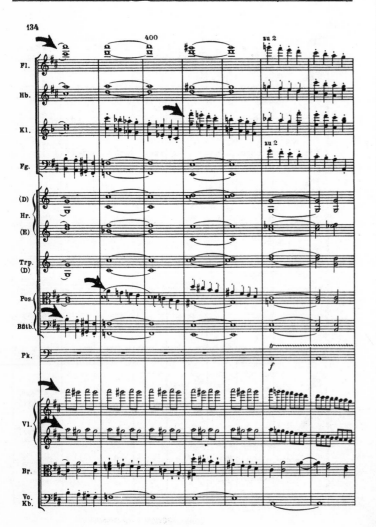

CODA—SECTION 5 〰〰〰

SYMPHONY No. 3, in F Major, Op. 90   *JOHANNES BRAHMS*

MOVEMENTS:

1. *Allegro con brio*
2. *Andante*
3. *Poco allegretto*
4. *Allegro*

The metronome marks for this symphony are indicated by the composer.

Symphony No. 3 is scored for the following instruments:

2 Flöten (Flutes)	*Fl.*	3 Posaunen (Trombones)	*Pos.*
2 Hoboen (Oboes)	*Hb.*	2 Pauken (Tympani)	*Pk.*
2 Klarinetten (Clarinets)	*Kl.*	1. Violinen (1st Violins)	*Vl.*
2 Fagotte (Bassoons)	*Fg.*	2. Violinen (2nd Violins)	
1 Kontrafagott		Bratschen (Violas)	*Br.*
(Double Bassoon)	*Kfg.*	Violoncelli (Violoncellos)	*Vc.*
4 Hörner (Horns)	*Hr.*	Kontrabässe (Double Basses)	*Kb.*
2 Trompeten (Trumpets)	*Tr.*		

Each instrument is listed above under its name in German (as printed on the first page of the score); its English equivalent, and the abbreviation used on succeeding pages of the score.

Johannes Brahms completed his Symphony in F Major, Op. 90 during the summer of 1883, but it is not known for how long he was working on the individual movements . There is a hint in the composer's letter dated September 15, 1883, that this symphony was perhaps partially reconstructed from an earlier work, as he writes: "If I can find any early sketches, I will send them to you as well". The third symphony is in direct contrast to the second symphony, being what may be termed heroic in character.

The first performance of the Symphony in F Major, Op. 90, took place at Vienna on December 2, 1883. As was the case with the Second Symphony, the Vienna Philharmonic Orchestra was under the direction of Hans Richter.

Critical opinion of both personal friends and the music press in Austria and Germany was almost unanimously favorable. The first presentation however, at the Vienna Philharmonic Concert, was marred by a hissing demonstration engineered by partisans of Bruckner and Wagner which only the marked enthusiasm of the major part of the audience was able to still.

Symphonie No 3

I

EXPOSITION
Allegro con brio

Johannes Brahms, Op. 90
1833–1897

6

8

SUBORDINATE THEME 〰〰〰〰〰〰〰〰〰〰〰〰〰〰

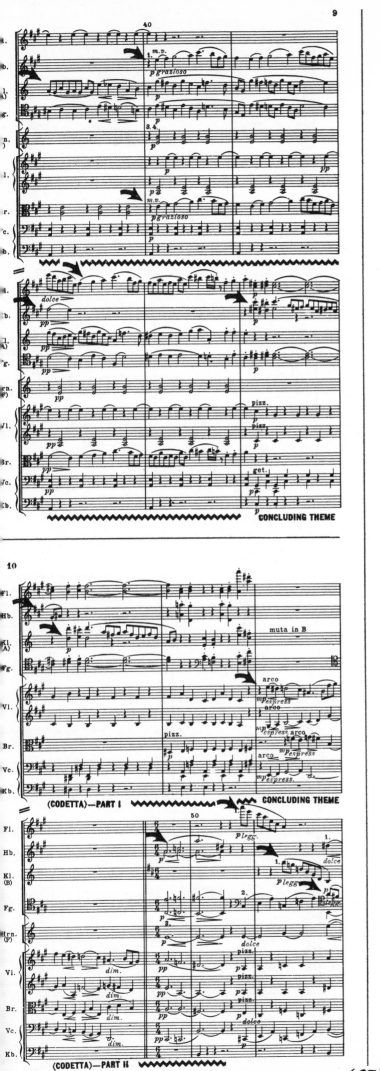

CONCLUDING THEME

(CODETTA)—PART I

CONCLUDING THEME

(CODETTA)—PART II

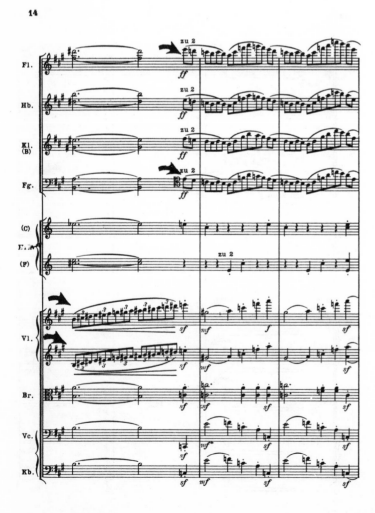

DEVELOPMENT

DEVELOPMENT—SECTION I 〜〜〜

DEVELOPMENT—SECTION 2

RETURN PRINCIPAL THEME 〰〰

BRIDGE PASSAGE 〰〰

RETURN CONCLUDING THEME (CODETTA)—PART I

RETURN CONCLUDING THEME (CODETTA)—PART II

RETURN SUBORDINATE THEME

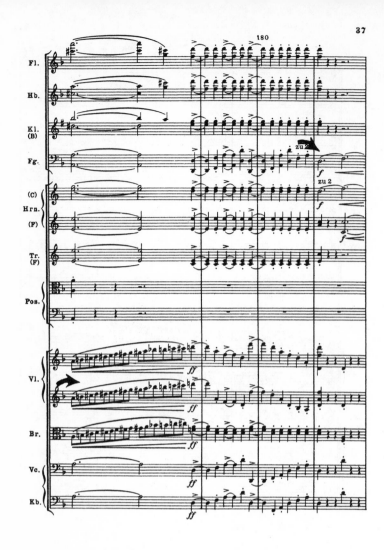

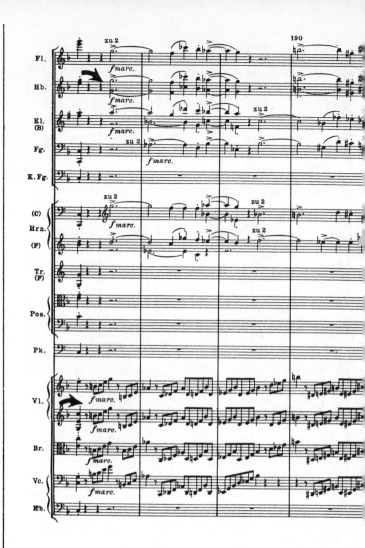

CODA—SECTION 2

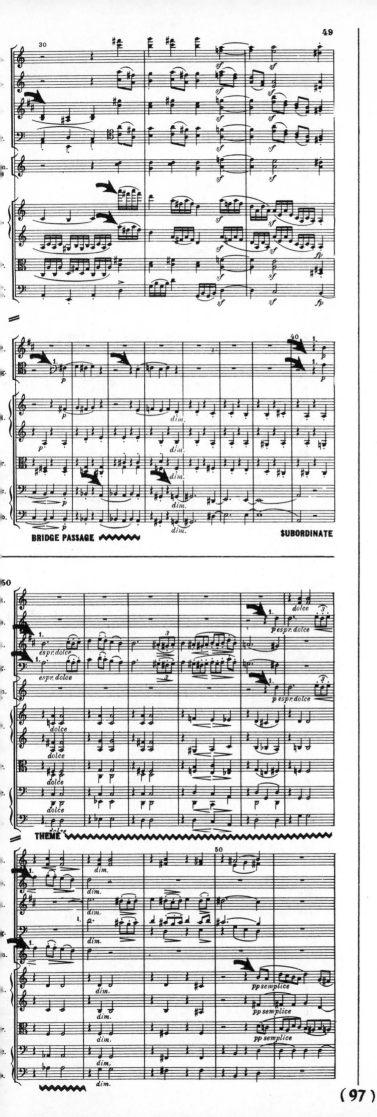

RETURN PRINCIPAL THEME

(99)

III
RONDO FORM
Poco Allegretto

2 Flöten
2 Hoboen
Klarinetten in B
2 Fagotte
Hörner in C
Violine I
Violine II
Bratsche
Violoncell
Kontrabaß

PRINCIPAL THEME

SUBORDINATE THEME

74

76

EXPOSITION **IV**

Allegro

BRIDGE PASSAGE ∿∿∿

SUBORDINATE THEME 〰〰〰〰〰〰〰〰〰〰〰〰〰〰〰〰〰〰〰〰

CONCLUDING THEME (CODETTA)

BRIDGE PASSAGE ∿∿∿∿

RETURN SUBORDINATE THEME

CODA—SECTION 2 ⋀⋀⋀

CODA—SECTION 3 〰〰〰

SYMPHONY No. 4, in E Minor, Op. 98   *JOHANNES BRAHMS*

MOVEMENTS:

1. *Allegro non troppo*
2. *Andante moderato*
3. *Allegro giocoso*
4. *Allegro energico e passionato*

The metronome marks for this symphony are indicated by the composer.

Symphony No. 4 is scored for the following instruments:

2 Flöten (Flutes)	*Fl.*	3 Posaunen (Trombones)	*Pos.*
2 Hoboen (Oboes)	*Hb.*	2 Pauken (Tympani)	*Pk.*
2 Klarinetten (Clarinets)	*Kl.*	1 Triangolo (Triangle)	*Trgl.*
2 Fagotte (Bassoons)	*Fg.*	1. Violinen (1st Violins)	
1 Kontrafagott		2. Violinen (2nd Violins)	*Vl.*
(Double Bassoon)	*Kfg.*	Bratschen (Violas)	*Br.*
4 Hörner (Horns)	*Hr.*	Violoncelli (Violoncellos)	*Vc.*
2 Trompeten (Trumpets)	*Tr.*	Kontrabässe (Double Basses)	*Kb.*

Each instrument is listed above under its name in German (as printed on the first page of the score); its English equivalent, and the abbreviation used on succeeding pages of the score.

Johannes Brahms composed the first and second movements of the Symphony in E Minor, Op. 98 during the summer of 1884; the third and fourth movements were completed in 1885. He seemed to realize the stern character of his work, for he wrote in his usually humorous way to Hans von Bulow as follows: "I am pondering whether the symphony will find more of a public. I fear it smacks of the climate of this country (the Styrian Alps in Austria); the cherries are not sweet here, and you would certainly not eat them".

The first performance of the Symphony in E Minor, Op. 98, took place at Meiningen on October 25, 1885. It was played by the Meiningen Orchestra under the drection of the composer; a week later it was repeated under the direction of Hans von Bulow.

Critical opinion of both personal friends and the music press was highly favorable after the first performance of the symphony, but several persons to whom Brahms played it on the piano previous to the concert, among them Hanslick, thought it altogether too serious in character.

SYMPHONIE № 4

I

Johannes Brahms, Op. 98
(1833-1897)

9

SUBORDINATE THEME—PART I 〰〰〰〰〰 SUBORDINATE

10

THEME—PART II, 1st PERIOD 〰〰〰〰〰〰〰〰〰

12

SUBORDINA

THEME—PART II, 2nd PERIOD 〰〰〰〰〰

85

CONCLUDING THEME (CODETTA)—PART I 〰〰〰〰〰〰

100

105

95

95

E
110

CONCLUDING THEME (CODETTA)—PART II 〰〰〰〰〰〰

DEVELOPMENT—SECTION I

DEVELOPMENT—SECTION 2

DEVELOPMENT—SECTION 5 〰〰〰

DEVELOPMENT—SECTION 8 〰〰〰

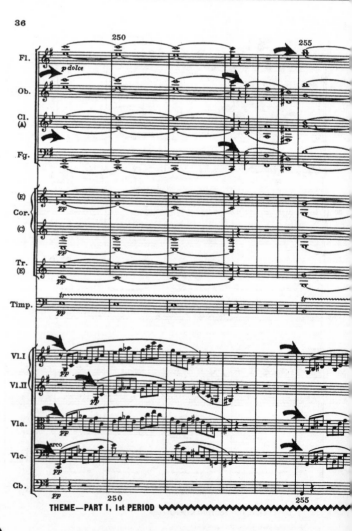

RETURN PRINCIPAL THEME—PART I, 2nd PERIOD

RETURN PRINCIPAL THEME—PART II, 1st PERIOD

RETURN PRINCIPAL THEME—PART II, 2nd PERIOD

BRIDGE PASSAGE

RETURN SUBORDINATE THEME—PART I ⌇⌇⌇ RETURN SUBORDINATE THEM

PART II, 1st PERIOD ⌇⌇⌇⌇⌇⌇⌇⌇⌇⌇⌇⌇⌇⌇

RETURN SUBORDINATE THEME—PART II, 2nd PERIOD 〰〰〰〰〰〰

RETURN CONCLUDING THEME (CODETTA)—PART I 〰〰〰〰〰〰

RETURN CONCLUDING THEME (CODETTA)—PART II 〰〰〰〰〰

CODA—SECTION 1 〰〰〰

CODA—SECTION 2 〰〰〰

CODA—SECTION 3 〰〰〰

II

INTRODUCTION

Andante moderato

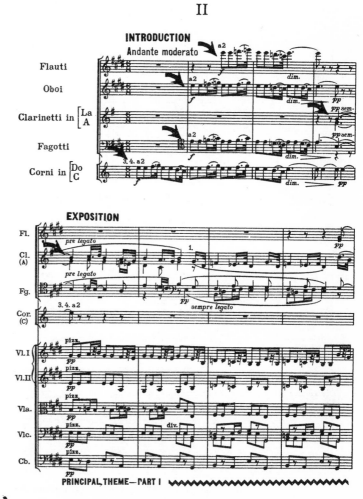

EXPOSITION

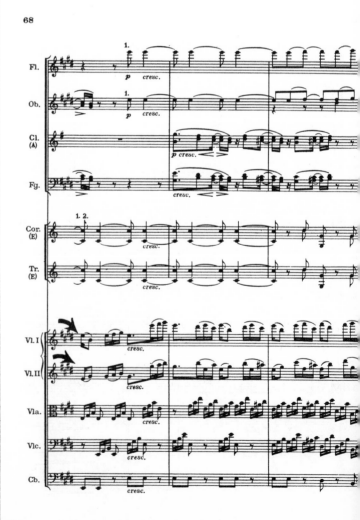

73

RETURN PRINCIPAL THE

— PART II

74 RECAPITULATION

RETURN PRINCIPAL THEME—PART I, 1st PERIOD

RETURN PRINCIPAL THEME—PART I, 2nd PERIOD

76

BRIDGE PASSAGE—PART I (NEW MATERIAL)

RETURN BRIDGE PASSAGE—PART II

III

EXPOSITION

Allegro giocoso

PRINCIPAL THEME—PART I

PRINCIPAL THEME—PART II 〰

BRIDGE PASSAGE

PRINCIPAL THEME—PART III 〰

SUBORDINATE THEME 〰

RECAPITULATION

RETURN PRINCIPAL THEME

—PART II

RETURN PRINCIPAL THEME—PART III

BRIDGE PASSAGE

RETURN SUBORDINATE THEME

CODA—SECTION 2 〰〰〰

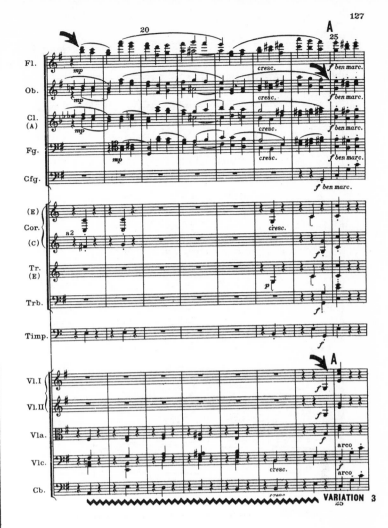

VARIATION 5

VARIATION 6

VARIATION 7

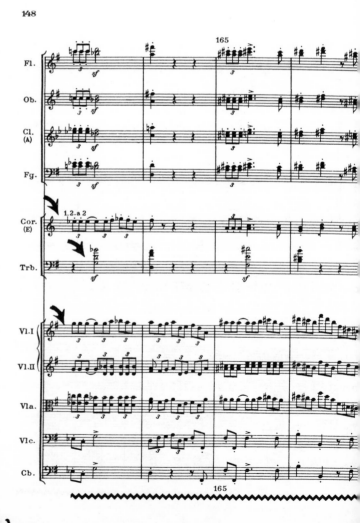

VARIATION 21

VARIATION 22

VARIATION 23

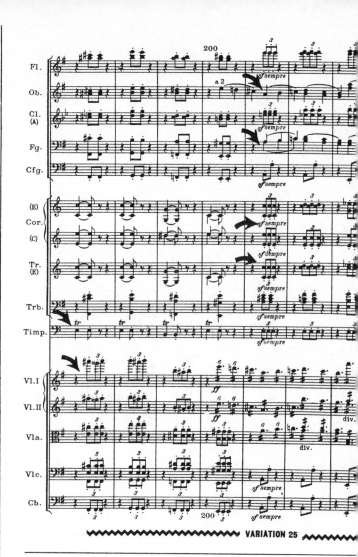

FOURTH SECTION

CODA

Più Allegro

VARIATION 31

VARIATION 32

VARIATION 34 · 300 · FINAL SECTION

VARIATION 33 · 295

168

SYMPHONY No. 4, in F Minor, Op. 36   *PETER ILICH TSCHAIKOWSKY*

MOVEMENTS:

1. *Andante Sostenuto—Moderato con anima*
2. *Andantino in modo di canzona*
3. *Scherzo-Pizzicato ostinato*
4. *Allegro con fuoco*

The metronome marks for this symphony are indicated by the composer.

Symphony No. 4 is scored for the following instruments:

2 Flöten (Flutes)	*Fl.*	1 Basstuba (Bass Tuba)	*Bsstb.*
2 Hoboen (Oboes)	*Hb.*	3 Pauken (Tympani)	*Pk.*
2 Klarinetten (Clarinets)	*Kl.*	1. Violinen (1st Violins)	*Vl.*
2 Fagotte (Bassoons)	*Fg.*	2. Violinen (2nd Violins)	
4 Hörner (Horns)	*Hr.*	Bratschen (Violas)	*Br.*
2 Trompeten (Trumpets)	*Tr.*	Violoncelli (Violoncellos)	*Vc.*
3 Posaunen (Trombones)	*Pos.*	Kontrabässe (Double Basses)	*Kb.*

Each instrument is listed above under its name in German (as printed on the first page of the score) ; its English equivalent, and the abbreviation used on succeeding pages of the score.

The score of Tschaikowsky's Fourth Symphony, completed in 1877, bears the dedication "To my best friend", referring to Madame Nadeshda von Meck, a wealthy widow who made it possible for the composer to devote himself exclusively to creative work by settling upon him an annuity of about three thousand dollars. In his correspondence with Madame von Meck, Tschaikowsky frequently spoke of the work as "our symphony", and, in a letter dated March, 1878, he sent her a complete outline of the ideas which form the basis for the entire work. The first movement depicts stern unrelenting fate, the second the pensive sadness of melancholy, the third has no definite program, but the Finale, the movement presented here, is "the picture of a folk-holiday, see how it feels to be jolly. Scarcely have you forgotten yourself before untiring Fate again announces its approach. The other children of men are not concerned with you. Rejoice in the happiness of others, and you can still live".

The first performance of the Symphony in F Minor, Op. 36, took place at St. Petersburg on February 10, 1878, at one of the concerts of the Russian Musical Society.

Critical opinion of personal friends, fellow composers and music journalists appears to have been almost unanimously unfavorable. Most of the critics did not even mention its performance; others recorded an indifferent success. The eminent Russian composer, Sergei Taneiev, in a letter to Tschaikowsky, disapproved of the length of the first movement, rather approved of the Andante, thought the Scherzo sounded too much like ballet music and disliked the Finale.

Symphonie Nº 4

I
INTRODUCTION
Andante sostenuto

P. Tschaikowsky, Op. 36
1840-1893

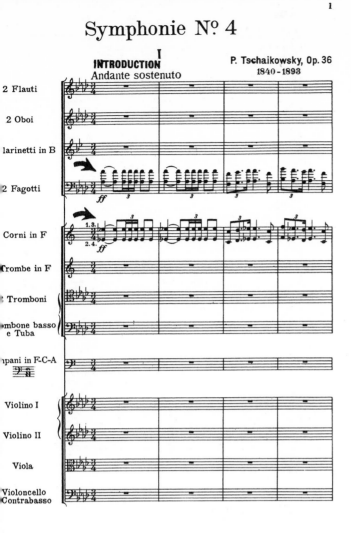

PRINCIPAL THEME—PART I.

1st PERIOD

PRINCIPAL THEME—PART I,

PRINCIPAL THEME—PART II, 3rd PERIOD

Moderato con anima (Tempo del comincio)

CONCLUDING THEME

(CODETTA)—PART I

30

32

CONCLUDING THEME (CODETTA)—PART II ᔨᔨᔨ

SECTION 5

DEVELOPMENT—SECTION 6

DEVELOPMENT—SECTION 7

RETURNING PASSAGE (RETRANSITION) ∿∿∿

RECAPITULATION

RETURN

53

Rallentando poco a poco

PRINCIPAL THEME—PART I, 1st PERIOD ∿∿∿∿∿∿∿∿∿

BRIDGE PASSAGE ∿∿∿∿∿

54

56

Moderato assai, quasi andante

RETURN SUBORDINATE THEME—PART I, 1st PERIOD ∿∿∿

(176)

Poco a poco stringendo

Allegro con anima

RETURN

SUBORDINATE THEME—PART II, 2nd PERIOD

RETURN CONCLUDIN

Sempre stringendo al -

THEME (CODETTA)—PART II

RETURN CONCLUDING THEME (CODETTA)—PART III

CODA

CODA—SECTION I

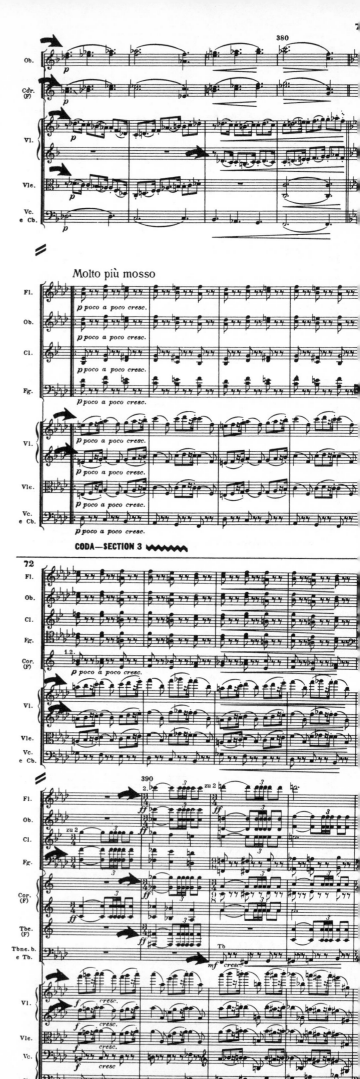

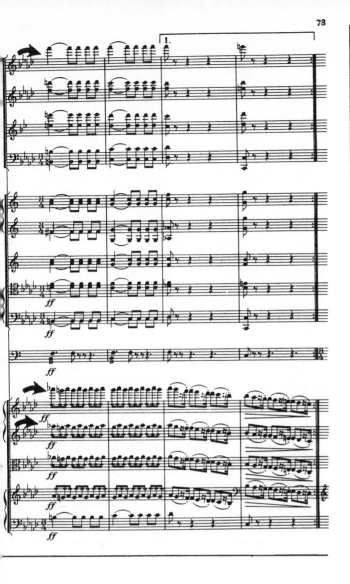

CODA—SECTION 4 ∿∿∿

Più mosso Allegro vivo

CODA—SECTION 5 ∿∿∿

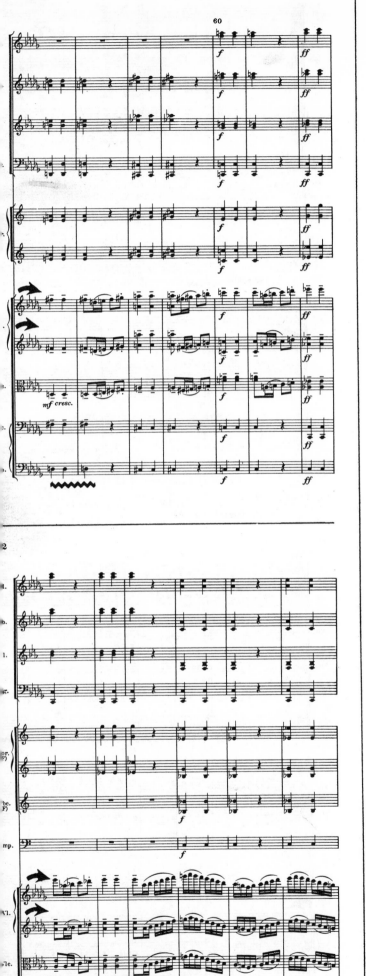

SUBORDINATE THEME—PART II, 1st PERIOD ∿∿∿∿∿

150

SUBORDINATE THEME—PART II, 2nd PERIOD ∿∿∿

∿∿∿∿∿ **SUBORDINATE THEME—PART II.**

160

3rd PERIOD ∿∿∿∿∿∿∿∿∿∿∿ **(185)**

Fl.
Ob.
Cl.
Fg.
Cor. (F)
Tbe. (F)
Timp.
Vl.
Vle.
Vc.
Cb.

170

∿∿∿∿ **SUBORDINATE THEME—PART III, 1st PERIOD** ∿∿∿∿

Fl.
Ob.
Cl.
Fg.
Cor. (F)
Tbe. (F)
Timp.
Vl.
Vle.
Vc.
Cb.

∿∿∿∿∿∿∿∿ **SUBORDINATE THEME—PART III,**

180

2nd PERIOD

190

RETURNING PASSAGE (RETRANSITION)

rit.

Tempo I
200

cantabile

pizz.

pizz.

pizz.

pizz.

RETURN PRINCIPAL THEME—PART I

210

tr

arco

arco

arco

arco

RETU

220

sf

PRINCIPAL THEME—PART II, 1st PERIOD

CODA—SECTION 1 ~~~~~

CODA—SECTION 3 (PRINCIPAL THEME—PART I) ~~~~~

CODA—SECTION 2 ~~~~~

CODA—SECTION 4 ~~~

III
Scherzo

(188)

CODA—SECTION 4

CODA—SECTION 3 〰〰〰

PRINCIPAL THEME—PART III, 2nd PERIOD 〰〰〰〰〰〰〰

PRINCIPAL THEME—PART III, 3rd PERIOD 〰〰〰

SUBORDINATE THEME—PART I

BRIDGE PASSAGE

SUBORDINATE THEME—PART I

(1st REPETITION)

SUBORDINATE THEME—PART I (2nd REPETITION)

SUBORDINATE THEME—PART I (3rd REPETITION)

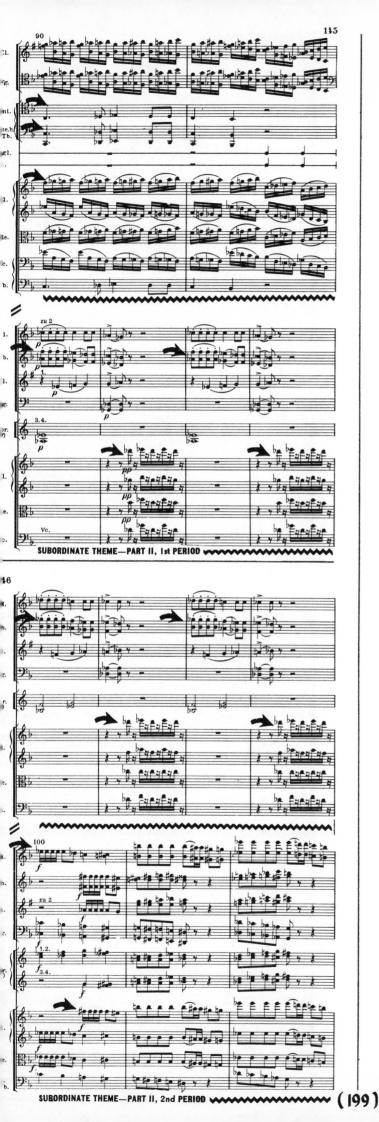

SUBORDINATE THEME—PART II, 1st PERIOD

SUBORDINATE THEME—PART II, 3rd PERIOD

SUBORDINATE THEME—PART II, 2nd PERIOD

(199)

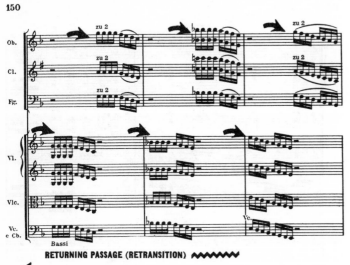

RETURN PRINCIPAL

THEME—PART III, 2nd PERIOD ᜵᜵᜵᜵᜵᜵᜵᜵᜵᜵

RETURN PRINCIPAL THEME—PART III, 3rd PERIOD ᜵᜵᜵᜵

RETURN SUBORDINATE THEME—PART I

FIRST REPETITION SUBORDINATE THEME—PART I

SECOND REPETITION SUBORDINATE THEME—PART I ∧

THIRD REPETITION SUBORDINATE THEME—PART I ∨ (203)

CODA—SECTION I ∼∼∼∼

CODA—SECTION 2 (RESTATEMENT INTRODUCTION — 1st MOVEMENT) ∿∿∿

CODA—SECTION 3 ∿∿∿

173

175

174

176

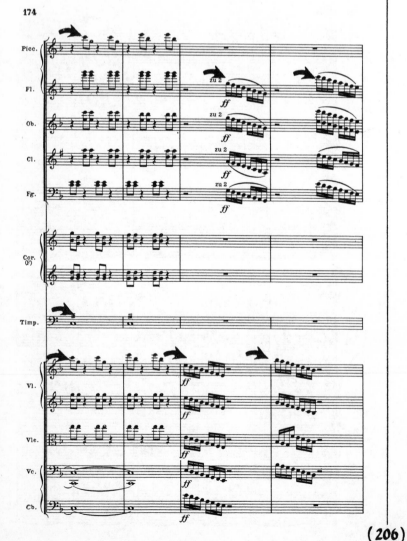

(206)

CODA—SECTION 5

CODA—SECTION 6

SYMPHONY No. 5, in E Minor, Op. 64   *PETER ILICH TSCHAIKOWSKY*

MOVEMENTS:

1. *Andante—Allegro con anima*
2. *Andante cantabile, con alcuna licenza*
3. *Allegro moderato*
4. *Andante maestoso—Allegro vivace*

The metronome marks for this symphony are indicated by the composer.

Symphony No. 5 is scored for the following instruments:

1 Kleine Flöte (Piccolo)	*kl.Fl.*	1 Basstuba (Bass Tuba)	*Bsstb.*
2 Flöten (Flutes)	*Fl.*	3 Pauken (Tympani)	*Pk.*
2 Hoboen (Oboes)	*Hb.*	1. Violinen (1st Violins)	*Vl.*
2 Klarinetten (Clarinets)	*Kl.*	2. Violinen (2nd Violins)	
2 Fagotte (Bassoons)	*Fg.*	Bratschen (Violas)	*Br.*
4 Hörner (Horns)	*Hr.*	Violoncelli (Violoncellos)	*Vc.*
2 Trompeten (Trumpets)	*Tr.*	Kontrabässe (Double Basses)	*Kb.*
3 Posaunen (Trombones)	*Pos.*		

Each instrument is listed above under its name in German (as printed on the first page of the score); its English equivalent, and the abbreviation used on succeeding pages of the score.

An interval of eleven years elapsed between Tschaikowsky's Fourth and Fifth symphonies; the latter was composed during 1888. The composer substituted a movement in waltz tempo for the usual *Scherzo,* and his letters to Madame Nadeshda von Meck during the period that he was engaged in creating the work indicate that he strove to bring it to the greatest possible state of perfection, and to avoid characteristic faults criticized in his previous symphonic works.

The first performance of the Symphony in E Minor, Op. 64, took place at St. Petersburg on November 16, 1888, the orchestra being under the direction of Tschaikowsky.

Critical opinion insofar as the Press was concerned appears to be somewhat divided. Perhaps the most interesting estimate was written by Berezovsky who says in part: "The Fifth Symphony is the weakest of all Tschaikowsky's symphonies; nevertheless it is a striking work, and takes a prominent place not only among Tschaikowsky's compositions, but among Russian musical works in general. . . . the entire symphony seems to set forth some dark spiritual experience, some heavy condition of a mind torn by importunate memories which have poisoned existence".

PRINCIPAL THEME—PART II, 2nd PERIOD ∿∿∿∿∿ (213)

13

PRINCIPAL THEME—PART

14

PRINCIPAL THEME—PART II, 3rd PERIOD

16

(214)

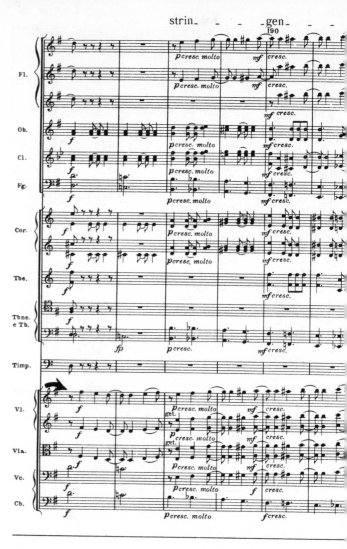

170 Molto più tranquillo (♩.=92)

SUBORDINATE THEME—PART II

180 zu 3

strin_ _ _gen_ _ _

190

do   al   Tempo I (♩.=104)

CONCLUDING THEME (CODETTA) ∿∿∿∿

DEVELOPMENT

DEVELOPMENT—SECTION I ∿∿∿∿

DEVELOPMENT—SECTION 2

DEVELOPMENT—SECTION 3 〜〜〜

DEVELOPMENT

—SECTION 6 〰〰〰

fff RETURNING

PASSAGE (RETRANSITION) ~~~~~~

RECAPITULATION

RETURN PRINCIPAL THEME—PART I ~~~~~~~~~~

RETURN PRINCIPAL THEME—PART II

Fl.
Ob.
Cl.
Fg.
Cor.
Tbe.
Tbne. e Tb.
Vl.
Vla.
Vc.
Cb.

360

RETURN PRINCIPAL THEME—PART III

Un pochettino più mosso

RETURN SUBORDINATE

THEME—PART I

Fl.
Ob.
Cl.
Fg.
Cor.
Vl.
Vla.
Vc.
Cb.

zu 3

Fl.
Ob.
Cl.
Fg.
Cor.
Vl.
Vla.
Vc.
Cb.

Molto più tranquillo come sopra

p molto cantabile ed espr.

Stringendo

Fl.
Ob.
Cl.
Fg.
Cor.
Tbe.
Tbne. e Tb.
Timp.
Vl.
Vla.
Vc.
Cb.

RETURN SUBORDINATE THEME—PART II (225)

CONCLUDING THEME (CODETTA) 〰〰〰〰

Tempo I

ᶠᶠᶠ RETURN

(226)

CODA—SECTION 3

II

INTRODUCTION
Andante cantabile, con alcuna licenza (♩. = 54)

PRINCIPAL THEME

SUBORDINATE THEME—PART II

Stringendo

Tempo precedente ($\quarternote$ = 100)

Tempo I

RETURNING PASSAGE (RETRANSITION) RETURN

PRINCIPAL THEME—PART I, 1st PERIOD

RETURN INTRODUCTION OF FIRST MOVEMENT

RETURN PRINCIPAL THEME—PART 1, 2nd PERIOD

REPETITION

PRINCIPAL THEME—PART I, 1st PERIOD

Un poco più animato (80)

Andante mosso ($\downarrow. = \downarrow = 66$)

RETURN CONCLUDING THEME (CODETTA)

ritenuto

animando · riten. ($\downarrow. = \downarrow = 66$)

102

104

RETURN INTRODUCTION OF FIRST MOVEMENT

Tempo I (♩.=54) CODA

Valse

III

PRINCIPAL SECTION
Allegro moderato (♩ = 138)

Flauti I II
Flauto III (Piccolo)
Oboi
Clarinetti in A
Fagotti
I II Corni in F
III IV
Trombe in A
Timpani in Fis-Cis
Violini I
Violini II
Viole
Violoncelli
Contrabassi

PRINCIPAL THEME—PART I, 1st PERIOD

PRINCIPAL THEME—PART

PRINCIPAL THEME—PART I, 2nd PERIOD

PRINCIPAL THEME—PART III, 1st PERIOD

PRINCIPAL THEME—PART III, 2nd PERIOD

TRIO

PRINCIPAL THEME—PART I

PRINCIPAL THEME—PART III, 3rd PERIOD

(241)

PRINCIPAL THEME—PART III ᐧᐧᐧᐧᐧᐧ

RETURN PRINCIPAL THEME—PART I, 1st PERIOD

RETURNING PASSAGE (RETRANSITION)

RETURN PRINCIPAL THEME—PART I, 2nd PERIOD

IV
Finale

INTRODUCTION
Andante maestoso ♩=80

Flauto I II	
Flauto III (Piccolo)	
Oboi	
Clarinetti in A	
Fagotti	
Corni in F {I II / III IV}	
Trombe in A	
Tromboni I II	
Tromboni III e Tuba	
Timpani in G·C·E	
Violini I	
Violini II	
Viola	
Violoncelli	
Contrabassi	

INTRODUCTION— 1st PERIOD 〜〜〜〜〜〜〜〜〜〜〜

—SECTION 2 〜〜〜〜〜

CODA—SECTION 3 〜〜〜〜〜

140

Cl.
Fg.
Cor.
Tb.
Vl.
Vla.
Vc.
Cb.

Cl.
Fg.
Cor.
Tb.
Vl.
Vla.
Vc.
Cb.

INTRODUCTION—2nd PERIOD 〜〜〜〜〜〜〜〜〜

EXPOSITION
Allegro vivace *(alla breve)*($\dot{} = 120$)

PRINCIPAL THEME—PART I, 1st PERIOD

PRINCIPAL THEME—PART I, 2nd PERIOD

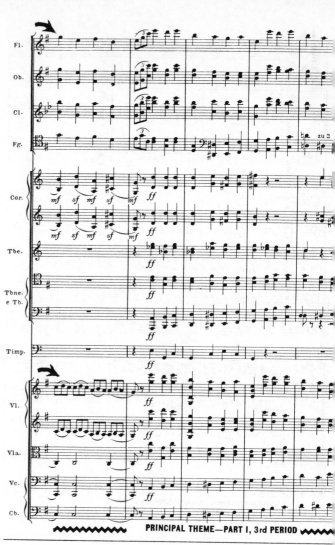

PRINCIPAL THEME—PART I, 3rd PERIOD

150

152

PRINCIPAL THEME—PAR

1st PERIOD

PRINCIPAL THEME—PART II, 2nd PERIOD

PRINCIPAL THEME—

PART II, 3rd PERIOD

Fl.

Ob.

Cl.

Fg.

Cor.

Tbe.

Tbne.
e Tb.

Timp.

Vl.

Vla.

Vc.

Cb.

Fl.

Ob.

Cl.

Fr.

Cor.

Tb.

Vl.

Vla.

Vc.

Cb.

SUBORDINATE THEME—PART II 〜〜〜〜〜

THEME (CODETTA) 〜〜〜〜〜〜〜〜〜〜〜〜〜〜〜〜〜〜〜〜〜

CONCLUDING

DEVELOPMENT

DEVELOPMENT—SECTION I

RETURNING PASSAGE (RETRANSITION) ∿∿∿

RECAPITULATION

Poco più animato

RETURN PRINCIPAL THEME—PART I, 1st PERIOD ∿∿∿∿∿∿∿

RETURN PRINCIPAL THEME—PART I, 3rd PERIOD

Tempo I

2nd PERIOD

RETURN PRINCIPAL THEME—PART II, 1st PERIOD

RETURN PRINCIPAL THEME—PART I,

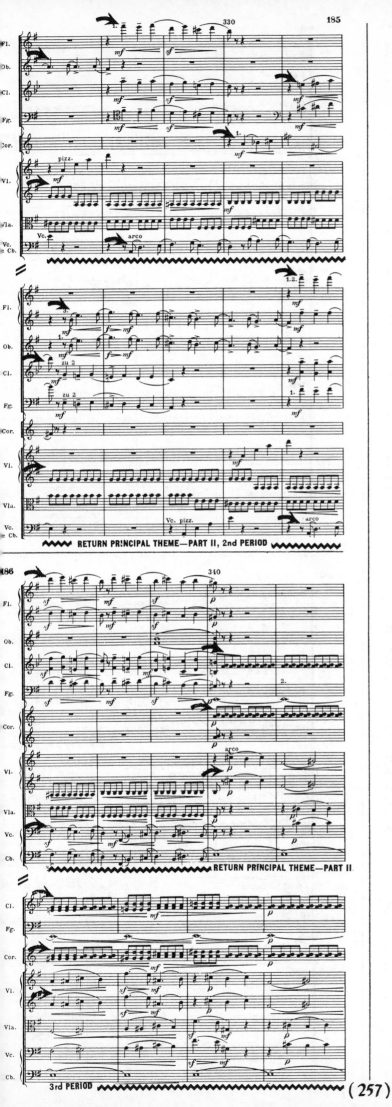

RETURN SUBORDINATE THEME—PART I, 1st PERIOD

RETURN SUBORDINATE THEME—PART II

RETURN SUBORD—

INATE THEME—PART I, 2nd PERIOD

198

420

200

CODA
Poco meno mosso

CODA—SECTION I

Molto vivace

CODA—SECTION 2

CODA—SECTION 3

460

Moderato assai e molto maestoso

CODA—SECTION 4 〰〰〰

riten. molto

470

Presto (♩=144)

CODA—SECTION 5 ᨑ

Fl.

Ob.

Cl.

Fg.

Cor.

Tbe.

Tbne.
e Tb.

Timp.

Vl.

Vla.

Vc.
e Cb.

510

520

Fl.

Ob.

Cl.

Fg.

Cor.

Tbe.

Tbne.
e Tb.

Vl.

Vla.

Vc.
e Cb.

Molto meno mosso (♩=96)

CODA—SECTION 6 〰〰〰〰

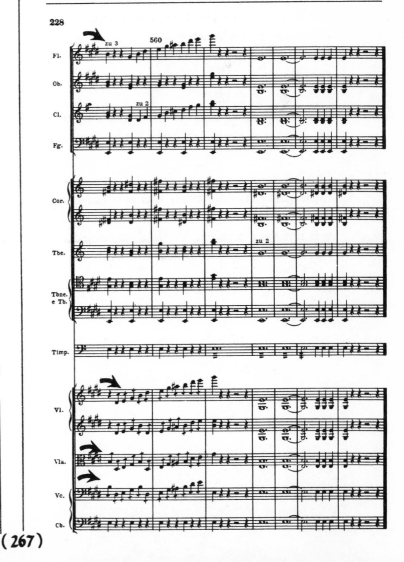

SYMPHONY No. 6, in B Minor, Op. 74 *PETER ILICH TSCHAIKOWSKY*

MOVEMENTS:

1. *Adagio—Allegro non troppo*
2. *Allegro con grazioso*
3. *Allegro molto vivace*
4. *Adagio lamentoso—Andante*

The metronome marks for this symphony are indicated by the composer.

Symphony No. 6 is scored for the following instruments:

1 Kleine Flöte (Piccolo) *kl.Fl.*	1 Basstuba (Bass Tuba) *Bsstb.*
2 Flöten (Flutes) *Fl.*	3 Pauken (Tympani) *Pk.*
2 Hoboen (Oboes) *Hb.*	1. Violinen (1st Violins) ⎫ *Vl.*
2 Klarinetten (Clarinets) *Kl.*	2. Violinen (2nd Violins) ⎭
2 Fagotte (Bassoons) *Fg.*	Bratschen (Violas) *Br.*
4 Hörner (Horns) *Hr.*	Violoncelli (Violoncellos) *Vc.*
2 Trompeten (Trumpets) *Tr.*	Kontrabässe (Double Basses) *Kb.*
3 Posaunen (Trombones) *Pos.*	

Each instrument is listed above under its name in German (as printed on the first page of the score); its English equivalent, and the abbreviation used on succeeding pages of the score.

The "Pathetique" Symphony was written by Tschaikowsky in 1893, and, having been completed just before his death, many writers are able to read in the music a program which would make the basis of the symphony autobiographical. It is supposed to contain the composer's premonition of his death, and a passage in the first movement, which is taken from the Russian Requiem, is construed as a memorial to his mother. All this naturally is hypothesis, as Tschaikowsky left no program for the work, nor did he name it the "Pathetique", although it is said that he gave his sanction to the subtitle.

The first performance of the Symphony in B Minor, Op. 74, took place at St. Petersburg on October 16, 1893, the orchestra being under the direction of Tschaikowsky.

Critical opinion at the first performance may be summarized in the statement that the work fell rather flat; the composer was applauded and recalled, but there was none of the enthusiasm usually displayed for a new Tschaikowsky work. One newspaper thought "the thematic material of the work was not very original, the leading subjects were neither new nor significant". Only one critic praised the work without qualification, while finding fault with the composer's conducting.

PRINCIPAL THEME—PART II

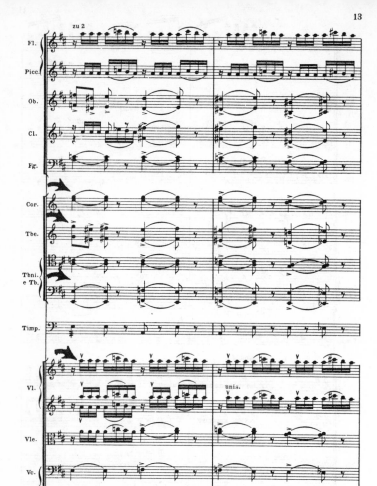

Moderato mosso (♩ = 100)

SUBORDINATE THEME—PART II

DEVELOPMENT—SECTION 2

DEVELOPMENT—SECTION 3

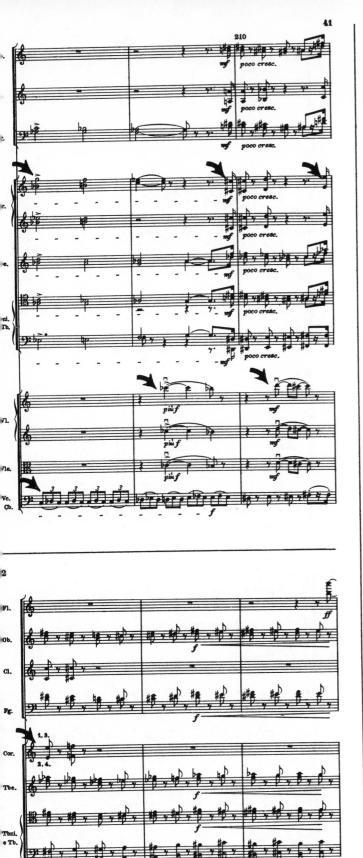

210

DEVELOPMENT—SECTION 6 〰〰〰

220

RETURNING PASSAGE (RETRANSITION) 〰〰〰

RETURN PRINCIPAL THEME

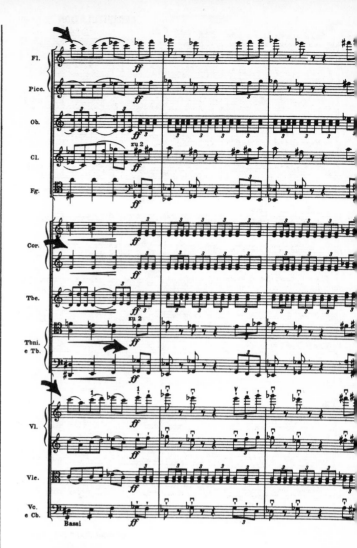

BRIDGE PASSAGE ∿∿∿

RETURN SUBORDINATE THEME—PART I ⋙

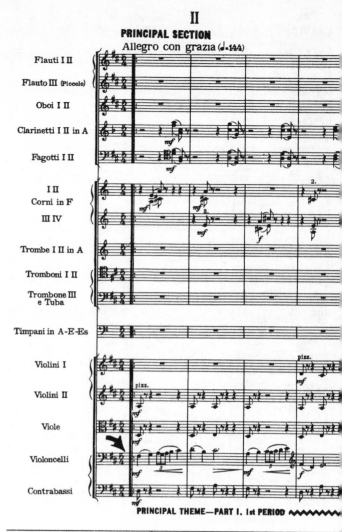

73

75

PRINCIPAL THEME—PART II, 2nd PERIOD ∿∿∿∿∿∿

PRINCIPAL THEME—PART II, 1st PERIOD ∿∿∿∿∿∿

PRINCIPAL THEME—PART III, 1st PERIOD ∿∿∿∿∿∿

PRINCIPAL THEME—PART III. 3rd PERIOD

PRINCIPAL THEME—PART III, 2nd PERIOD

TRIO *dolcezza e flebile*

PRINCIPAL THEME—PART I

PRINCIPAL THEME—PART II

PRINCIPAL THEME—PART III, 1st PERIOD

PRINCIPAL THEME—PART III, 2nd PERIOD

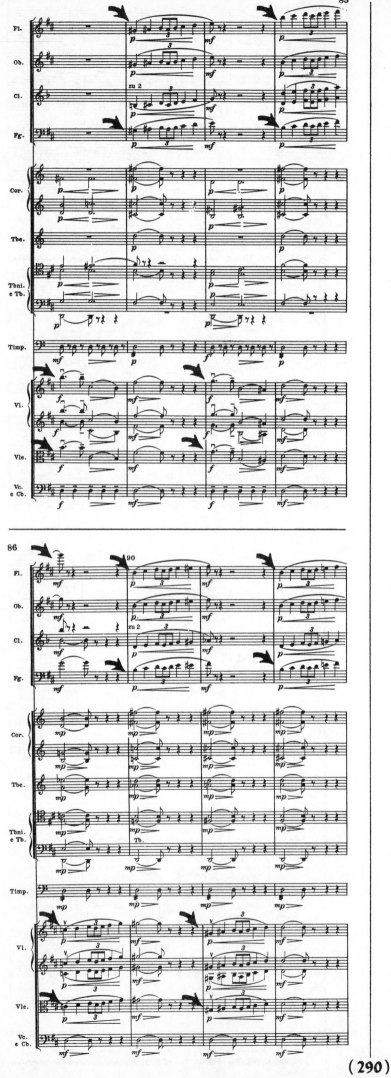

RETURN PRINCIP

RETURN PRINCIPAL THEME—PART II

RETURN PRINCIPAL THEME—PART III

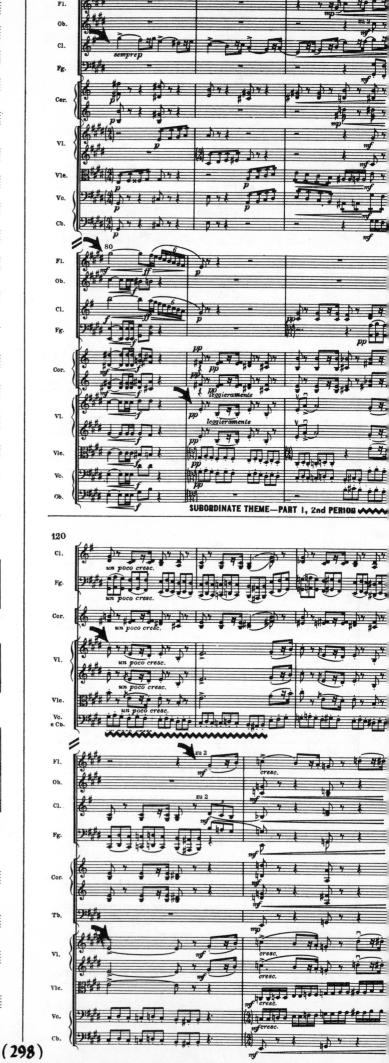

SUBORDINATE THEME—PART I, 1st PERIOD 〰〰〰〰〰〰〰〰

SUBORDINATE THEME—PART I, 2nd PERIOD 〰〰〰〰

SUBORDINATE THEME—PART II, 1st PERIOD

SUBORDINATE THEME—PART II,

131

RECAPITULATION

140

RETURN PRINCIPAL THEME—PART I , 1st PERIOD

132

RETURN PRINCIPAL THEME—PART I , 2nd PERIOD

RETURN PRINCIPAL THEME—PART II, 1st PERIOD

RETURN PRINCIPAL THEME—PART II, 2nd PERIOD

RETURN PRINCIPAL THEME—PART III

BRIDGE PASSAGE

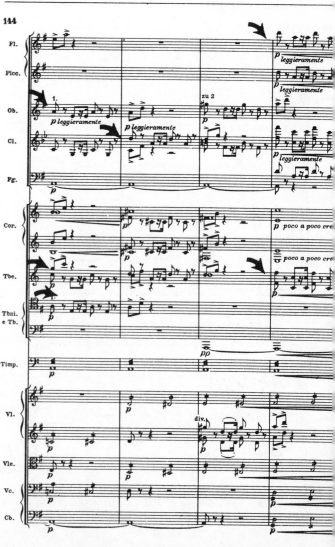

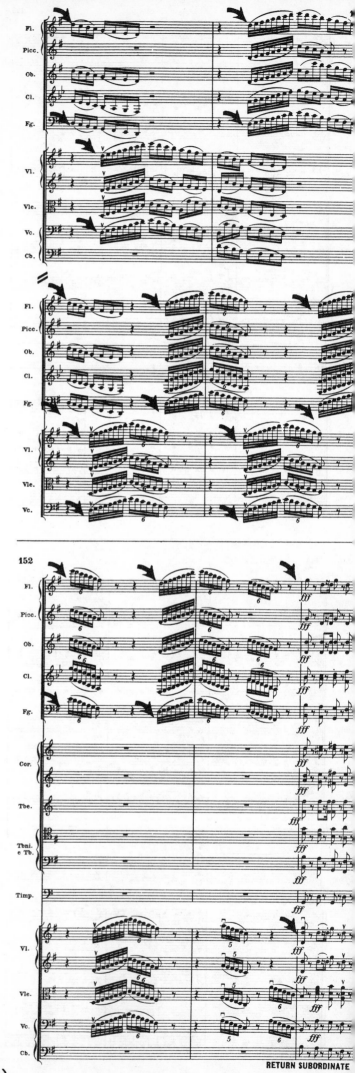

THEME—PART I

157

RETURN SUBORDINATE THEME—PART II ⌇⌇⌇⌇⌇⌇⌇⌇

158

160

(308)

161

RETURN SUBORDINATE THEME

— PART III

BRIDGE PASSAGE 〰

CODA—SECTION I 〰〰〰

CODA—SECTION 2 〰〰〰

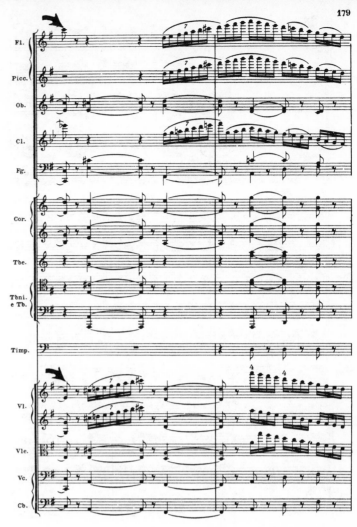

CODA—SECTION 3 〰〰〰

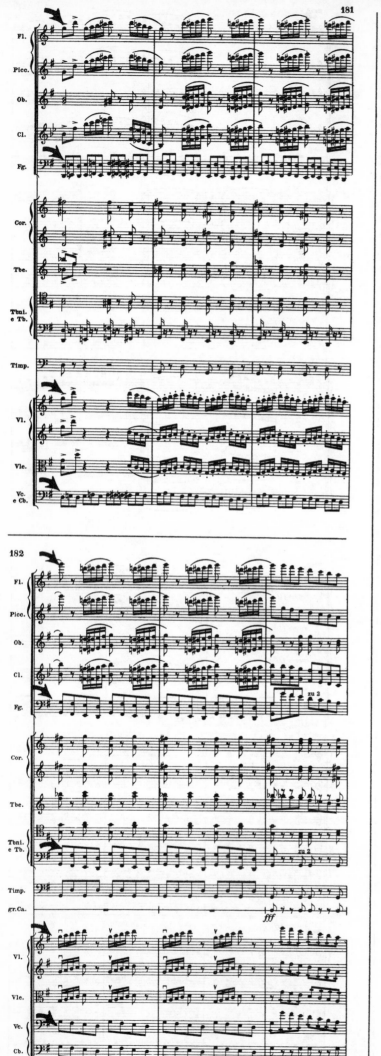

IV
Finale

EXPOSITION

Stringendo

Andante (♩ = 76)

Vivace

RETURNING PASSAGE (RETRANSITION) 〰〰

RECAPITULATION Andante non tanto (♩ = 60)

RETURN PRINCIPAL THEME—PART I 〰〰

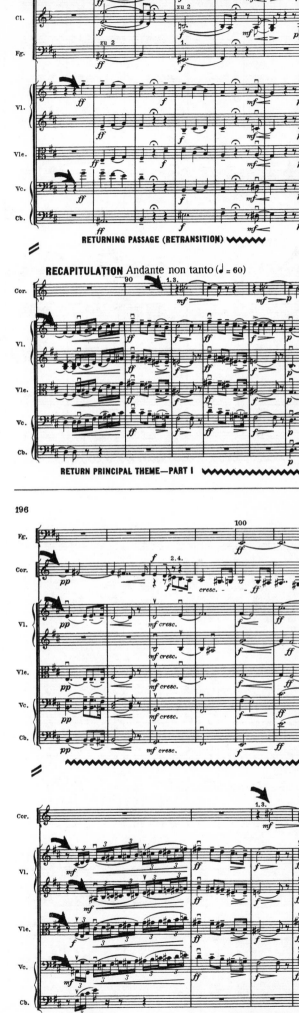

RETURN PRINCIPAL THEME—PART II 〰〰